Types of Animals

1. Name as many animals as you can.

2. Use this page to write or draw as many **different** animals as you can think of.

Animals are Living Things

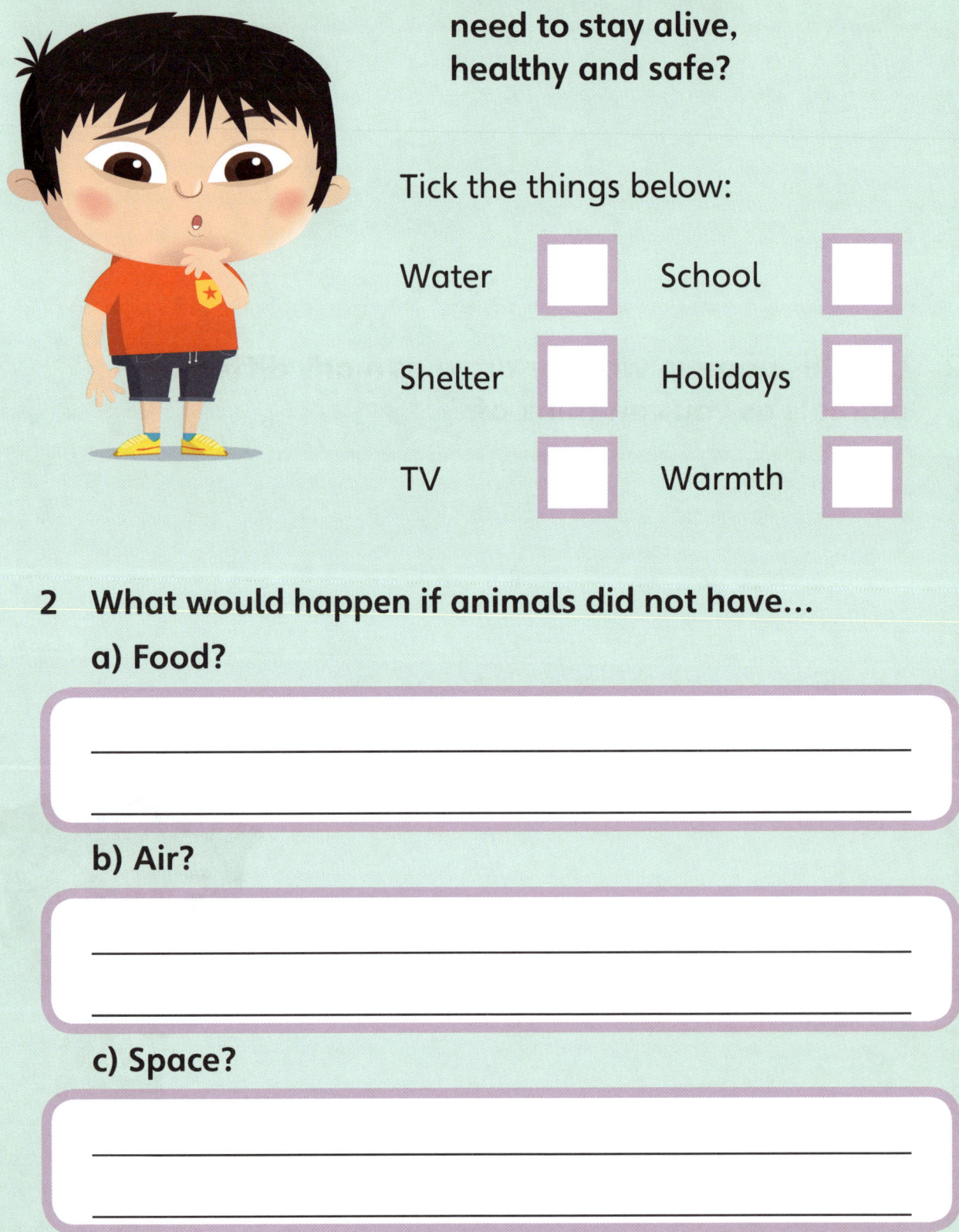

1 What do animals need to stay alive, healthy and safe?

Tick the things below:

Water ☐   School ☐

Shelter ☐   Holidays ☐

TV ☐   Warmth ☐

2 What would happen if animals did not have…

a) Food?

_____
_____

b) Air?

_____
_____

c) Space?

_____
_____

Animal or Not?

1. Name three **features** that an animal can have.

2. Draw a line from each picture to the correct column of the table.

Animal	Not an animal

3. Draw two more things that are 'animals' and 'not an animal'.

Where do Animals Live?

The place where a living thing lives is called a **habitat**.

1. **Match the animal to its habitat.**

Desert   Ocean   Arctic

2. **Draw an animal that might live in these habitats.**

Mountains

Pond

Forest

Looking for Animals

1. List the animals you think are living around your school.

   _____
   _____
   _____
   _____

Class 1 went looking for birds and mini-beasts around their school.

They recorded what they found in a table.

	Tally	Total
Birds	IIIII IIIII I	
Mini-beasts	IIIII IIIII IIIII IIII	

2. Complete the final column of the table to show how many birds and mini-beasts they found.

Animals in Zoos

1 Which animals can you find in a zoo?

2 Use this page to draw a poster to tell people about your zoo and the animals in it. Choose different animals from around the world.

Science Skills

Chart it!

Use this page to record the results for your class's favourite zoo animal:

Animal	Number of votes

1 Which is your class's favourite zoo animal?

2 How many children voted?

Animal Features

1 Draw your face, including as many different features as you can.

Compare the features of your face with another person in your class.

2 What is the same about your features?

3 What is different about your features?

Types of Animals

4 Who am I?

a
Who am I? I have no legs.
I have fins.
I am gold, yellow or orange coloured.
I have scales on my body.

I am a _____

b
Who am I? I have four legs.
I have long eyelashes.
I have a long tail.
I have a hump (or two) on my back.

I am a _____

5 Make up your own 'Who am I?' questions for another person in your class to guess.

_____
_____
_____
_____
_____

Animal Groups

1 Describe the features of an animal in each group:

a I am a **mammal** and I have...

b I am a **fish** and I have...

c I am a **bird** and I have...

d I am an **amphibian** and I have...

e I am a **reptile** and I have...

Types of Animals

2 Circle the group of animals you would like to find out more about:

fish   birds   mammals   reptiles   amphibians

Use this page to make notes about your animal group.

Animals at Home

1. Draw a line from each animal to show whether it would make a good **pet** or not.

| Good pet | Not a good pet | Not sure |

2. I think that a _____ would make a good pet because _____
_____

3. I think that a _____ would *not* make a good pet because _____
_____

Animals in the Arabian Desert

1 Which animals can be found living in the Arabian Desert?

   _____
   _____
   _____

2 Why do parts of the Arabian Desert have no fish or amphibians?

   _____
   _____
   _____

3 Look at the animals below. Which do you think is the odd one out? Why?

   _____
   _____
   _____

Sand cat   Jackal   Hare

What do Animals Eat?

1. Write the name of the animal in the correct circle.

   giraffe   human   polar bear
   shark   rhino   monkey

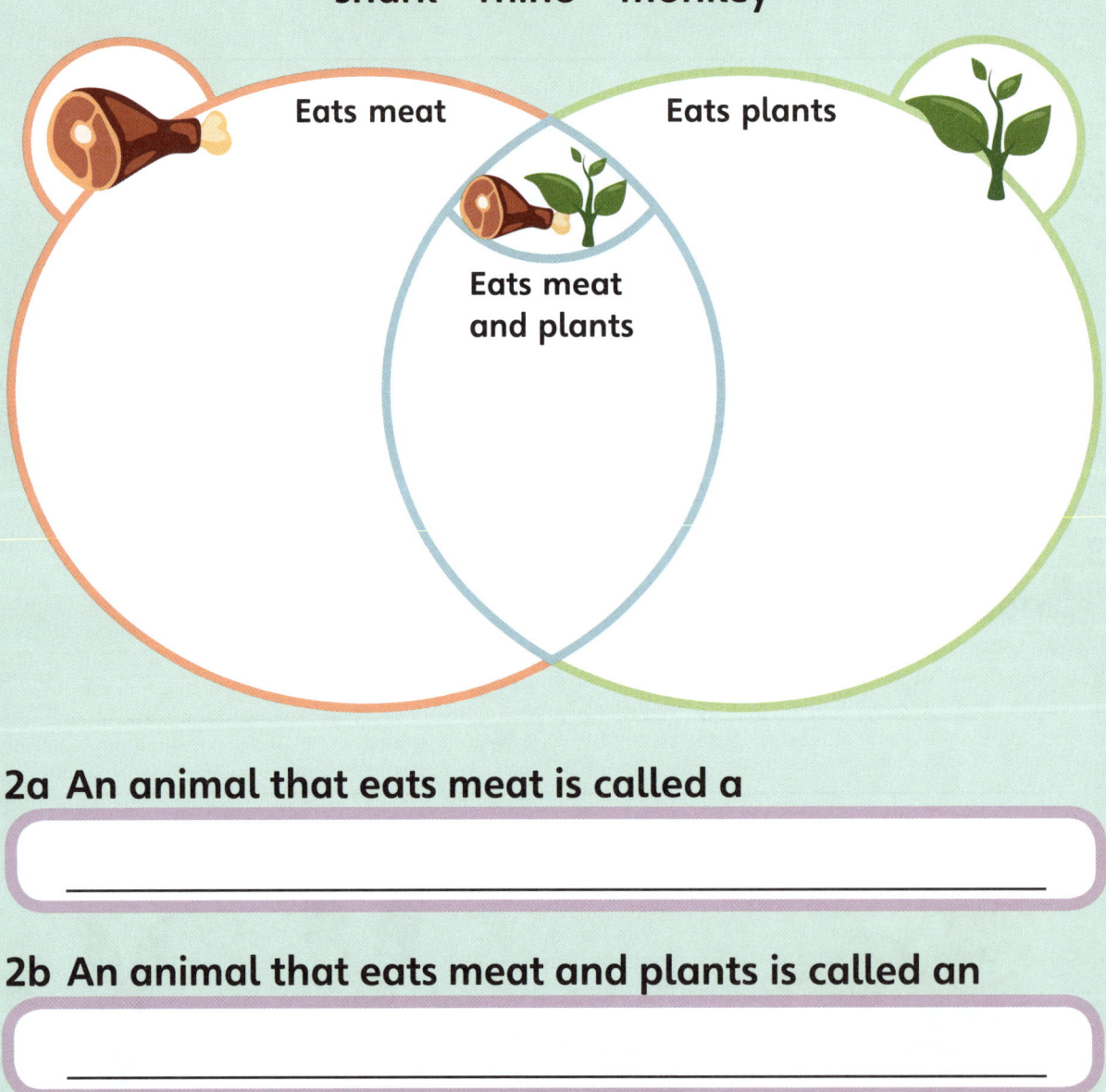

2a An animal that eats meat is called a

2b An animal that eats meat and plants is called an

2c An animal that eats plants is called a

A Day in the Life of a Zookeeper

1 What do you think a zookeeper does at 5:00 pm?

2 What do you think a zookeeper does at 10:00 pm?

Use this space to plan a map for your zoo.

What I Know About Types of Animals

1. Write down all the animals you know for the letters of the alphabet.

a b c	d e f	g h i	j k l
m n o	p q r	s t u	v w x y z

Use coloured pencils to shade:
mammals = brown
fish = blue
birds = red
reptiles = yellow
amphibians = green

INTERNATIONAL

Fuel curiosity, spark imagination.

UK National Curriculum YEAR 1 **Pearson iCURRICULUM YEAR 1, 3**

Science Bug International is an exciting and comprehensive science programme that has been designed to make sure your children never stop asking questions about their world!

This Workbook contains questions from the Topic Book plus additional questions to reinforce and extend learning.

With full and comprehensive coverage of the skills and knowledge required for curriculum attainment, *Science Bug International* will help you to nurture and inspire your young scientist.

Series editor: Deborah Herridge
Author: Nicky Waller

www.pearsonschools.co.uk
myorders@pearson.com

ISBN 978-0-435-19704-9